SALE NUMBER 3096

CATALOGUE PRICE $7 · BY MAIL $8.50

FREE PUBLIC EXHIBITION

From Friday · October 16 to Date of Sale
10 a.m. to 5 p.m. · Wednesday until 1 p.m.
Closed Sunday and Monday

PUBLIC AUCTION

Wednesday · October 21 at 8 p.m.

> ADMISSION TO MAIN SALESROOM BY CARD ONLY. CARD
> TO BE OBTAINED BY APPLICATION TO THE GALLERIES.

EXHIBITION & SALE AT THE

PARKE-BERNET GALLERIES · INC.

980 MADISON AVENUE · 76TH-77TH STREET

NEW YORK 10021

TELEPHONE 212/879-8300

✦   ✦   ✦

Sales Conducted by
PETER WILSON · JOHN L. MARION · MARCUS LINELL
EDWARD LEE CAVE · EDWARD J. LANDRIGAN III
KIRK A. IGLER · ROBERT C. WOOLLEY

1970

PORTRAIT OF THE LATE MRS IRMA N. STRAUS

BY PHILIP DE LASZLO

Highly Important
OLD MASTER DRAWINGS

INCLUDING EXAMPLES BY

FRANÇOIS BOUCHER · JEAN HONORE FRAGONARD
FRANCESCO GUARDI · JEAN AUGUSTE DOMINIQUE INGRES
GIOVANNI BATTISTA TIEPOLO · JEAN ANTOINE WATTEAU

Collected by the Late
MRS IRMA N. STRAUS
and
Her Late Husband
AMBASSADOR JESSE ISIDOR STRAUS

SOLD BY ORDER OF THE EXECUTORS OF HER ESTATE

JACK I. STRAUS · ROBERT K. STRAUS · ROBERT L. LEVY · ABRAHAM L. BIENSTOCK

Public Auction
Wednesday Evening · October 21 at 8 p.m.

PARKE-BERNET GALLERIES · INC
[*Affiliated with* SOTHEBY & CO *London*]
New York · 1970

THE BOUDOIR AT 720 PARK AVENUE

RESIDENCE OF THE LATE AMBASSADOR AND MRS JESSE ISIDOR STRAUS

FOREWORD

Mrs Jesse Straus cared passionately about individual works of art.

Although she did not own a very large number, their variety was astonishing. She had bought some of the largest textiles and some of the smallest enamels, important works by the most popular artists and objects exquisite but anonymous. It was an assemblage of objects about each of which she cared individually, unified by the consistency of her taste.

They will never be brought together again because they have been distributed where she thought they would do the most good. Most of the paintings went to the Metropolitan but not a Bouts which she believed New York did not need. The Fogg Museum received a splendid Gothic tapestry because it extended a series they already owned. Another tapestry went to the Louvre. In each case she believed the gift would provide a unique enrichment to the collection.

But her drawings were not given away. No one who visited Mrs Straus in her apartment could fail to recognize her particular involvement with them. It was among these she lived, especially during the later years of her long life.

Although the group is varied Mrs Straus clearly had a strong preference for the 18th Century, particularly French art of that period where she felt most at home. Here she added to her masterpieces works of lesser reputation because they pleased her regardless of the label.

The combination of a full appreciation of accepted standards with independence of taste is characteristic of great collectors. It is in exploring the mysteries of personal preferences that new values are most likely to be discovered. In providing other collectors with this opportunity Mrs Straus was exemplifying in the field of drawings her concept of the function of works of art. They should be a means to individual inspiration, not the blocks out of which a personal memorial can be built.

JOHN P. COOLIDGE
Professor of Fine Arts
Harvard University

CONDITIONS OF SALE

The property listed in this catalogue will be offered and sold by Parke-Bernet Galleries, Inc. ("Galleries") as agent for the "Consignor" on the following terms and conditions:

1. The Galleries and the Consignor assume no risk, liability or responsibility for the authenticity of the authorship of any property identified in this catalogue (that is, the identity of the creator or the period, culture, source or origin, as the case may be, with which the creation of any property is identified herein).

All property is sold "as is" and neither the Galleries nor the Consignor makes any warranties or representations of any kind or nature with respect to the property, and in no event shall they be responsible for the correctness, nor deemed to have made any representation or warranty, of description, genuineness, attribution, provenance or condition of the property and no statement in the catalogue or made at the sale or in the bill of sale or invoice or elsewhere shall be deemed such a warranty or representation or an assumption of liability.

2. Notwithstanding the preceding condition, if within twenty-one (21) days of the sale of any lot, the purchaser gives notice in writing to the Galleries that the lot so sold is a counterfeit and, if within fourteen (14) days after such notice the purchaser returns the lot to the Galleries in the same condition as when sold, and proves beyond reasonable doubt that the returned lot is in fact a counterfeit and that this was not indicated by a fair reading of the catalogue, the Galleries as agent for the Consignor will rescind the sale and refund the purchase price received by them.

PRINTED BOOKS which prove upon collation to be defective in text or illustration (provided such defects are not mentioned in the sale catalogue) may be returned by the purchaser, and the sale set aside, provided they are received back within twenty-one (21) days after the conclusion of the sale, in the same condition they were at the time of sale. No imperfect book will be taken back unless a note accompanies each book stating its imperfections, with the number of the lot and the date on which it was purchased. The return of books will not be accepted on account of damage to binding, stains, foxing, marginal wormholes, lack of blank leaves or other conditions not affecting the completeness of the text, nor on account of lack of list of plates, inserted advertisements, cancels or any subsequently published volume, supplement, appendix or plates, nor (provided the book be perfect) on account of an error in the enumeration of the plates. UNTITLED BOOKS in lots are sold "as is" and are not subject to return for any reason.

Descriptions of MANUSCRIPTS should not be taken as implying or guaranteeing that the manuscript is complete unless this is specifically stated.

3. The Galleries reserves the right to withdraw any property at any time before actual sale.

4. Unless otherwise announced by the auctioneer at the time of sale, all bids are per lot as numbered in the printed catalogue.

5. The Galleries reserves the right to reject a bid from any bidder. The highest bidder acknowledged by the auctioneer shall be the purchaser. In the event of any dispute between bidders, the auctioneer shall have sole and final discretion either to determine the successful bidder or to re-offer and resell the article in dispute. If any dispute arises after the sale, the Galleries' sale record shall be conclusive in all respects.

6. If the auctioneer determines that any opening bid is not commensurate with the value of the article offered, he may reject the same and withdraw the article from sale: and if, having acknowledged an opening bid, he decides that any advance thereafter is not of sufficient amount, he may reject the advance.

7. On the fall of the auctioneer's hammer, title to the offered lot or article will pass to the highest bidder who, thereupon (a) assumes full risk and responsibility therefor, (b) will sign a confirmation of purchase thereof, and (c) will pay the full purchase price therefor or such part as the Galleries may require. All property shall be removed from the Galleries by the purchaser at his expense not later than three days following its sale and, if not so removed, may be sent by the Galleries to a public warehouse for the account, risk and expense of the purchaser. If the foregoing Conditions or any other applicable conditions herein are not complied with, in addition to other remedies available to the Galleries and the Consignor by law, including without limitation the right to hold the purchaser liable for the bid price, the Galleries, at its option, may either (a) cancel the sale, retaining as liquidated damages all payments made by the purchaser or (b) resell the property on three days notice to the purchaser and for the account and risk of the purchaser, either publicly or privately, and in such event the purchaser shall be liable for the payment of any deficiency plus all costs, including warehousing, the expenses of both sales, and the Galleries' commission at its regular rates and all other charges due hereunder and incidental damages.

8. Unless the sale is advertised and announced as a sale without reserves, each lot is offered subject to reserve and the Galleries may bid through its representatives as agent for the Consignor.

9. Unless exempted by law from the payment thereof, the purchaser will be required to pay the combined New York State and local sales tax. The rate of such combined tax is 6 per cent if within New York City and ranges from 3 per cent to 6 per cent if outside New York City but within New York State.

Deliveries outside of New York State may be subject to the compensating use tax of another state and, where a duty of collection is imposed upon them by law, the Galleries will require payment of such taxes.

GLOSSARY

The following are examples of the terminology used in this catalogue. PLEASE NOTE THAT ALL STATEMENTS IN THIS CATALOGUE AS TO AUTHORSHIP, PERIOD, CULTURE, SOURCE OF ORIGIN ARE QUALIFIED STATEMENTS AND ARE MADE SUBJECT TO THE PROVISIONS OF THE CONDITIONS OF SALE INCLUDING THE FIRST CONDITION STATING THAT THE GALLERIES AND THE CONSIGNOR DO NOT WARRANT AND ASSUME NO RISK, LIABILITY OR RESPONSIBILITY FOR THE AUTHENTICITY OF THE AUTHORSHIP, THE DESCRIPTION, GENUINENESS, ATTRIBUTION, PROVENIENCE, PERIOD, CULTURE, SOURCE, ORIGIN OR CONDITION OF ANY PROPERTY IDENTIFIED IN THIS CATALOGUE.

a "*CLAUDE HOIN" — followed, under the heading AUTHORSHIP, by the words "ascribed to the named artist".
The work is ascribed to the named artist either by an outside expert or by our own staff and such ascription is accepted as reliable by the Galleries. While this is our highest category of authenticity in the present catalogue, and is assigned only upon exercise of our best judgment, no unqualified statement as to authorship is made or intended.

b SCHOOL OF CLAUDE HOIN
In our best judgment a work by a pupil or close follower of the artist.

c Signed
A work which has a signature which in our best judgment is a recognized signature of the artist.

d Dated
A work which is so dated and in our best judgment was executed at that date.

INDEX OF ARTISTS

All measurements are given with the height preceding the width. In catalogue
descriptions, "L." is an abbreviation for F. Lugt, *Les Marques de
Collection de Dessins et d'Estampes,* Amsterdam, 1921.

EVENING SESSION
Wednesday · October 21, 1970 at 8 p.m.
CATALOGUE NUMBERS 1 TO 50

*SIMON BENING

1 *THE ANNUNCIATION* and *THE VISITATION*
   gouache on vellum, a pair, mounted in one frame, arched

   each: 4¼ x 2½ *inches*
   110 x 62 mm

   Provenance

   Edouard Kann (no. 18)

FLEMISH SCHOOL, CIRCA 1500

2 *THE EDUCATION OF THE VIRGIN*
a miniature, *gouache on vellum*

$5\frac{1}{4} \times 3\frac{1}{8}$ *inches*
133 x 82 mm

Provenance

Edouard Kann

FRENCH SCHOOL, CIRCA 1510

3 *THE BIRTH OF THE VIRGIN*
   a leaf from an illuminated manuscript, *gouache on vellum*

7¼ x 5¼ *inches*
185 *x* 135 *mm*

aunit eft vng lacntrt dgeo
gaudni auumiauit a huirc
commindatter en actis eft feit uftiac
chistus deus noftrer qui folinens nate

FRENCH SCHOOL, CIRCA 1510

4 *ALL SAINTS*
   a leaf from an illuminated manuscript, *gouache on vellum*

                                                    7¼ x 5¼ inches
                                                    185 x 135 mm

*BALDASSARE PERUZZI

5 *AN ALLEGORY OF LIBERALITY*
*pen and brown ink and brown wash, heightened with white, squared for transfer on
pink tinted paper*

12½ x 7¼ inches
318 x 185 mm

Provenance

Sir Peter Lely (L.2092)
Prosper Henry Lankrink (L.2090)
Earl of Pembroke (sale: Sotheby's July 9, 1917, no. 397/5, as School of Raphael)

Literature

S. A. Strong, *Reproductions in facsimile of drawings by the old masters in the collection of
the Earl of Pembroke and Montgomery*, London, 1900, no. 59
Christoph Luitpold Frommel, *Baldassare Peruzzi als Maler und Zeichner, Munich*,
1967/68, no. 66C, pl. XLII D

**AUTHORSHIP. Ascribed to the named artist—subject to the qualifications set forth in
the GLOSSARY and CONDITIONS OF SALE, front of this Catalogue.*

8

*BALDASSARE PERUZZI

6 *AN ALLEGORY OF JUSTICE*
*pen and brown ink and brown wash, heightened with white, squared for transfer,
on pink tinted paper*

12½ x 7¼ *inches*
318 x 185 *mm*

Provenance

Sir Peter Lely (L.2092)
Prosper Henry Lankrink (L.2090)
Earl of Pembroke (sale: Sotheby's July 9, 1917, no. 397/5, as School of Raphael)

Literature

Strong, *op. cit.*, no. 59
Frommel, *op. cit.*, no. 66 B, pl. **XLII C**

*BALDASSARE PERUZZI

7 *AN ALLEGORY OF PRUDENCE*
pen and brown ink and brown wash, heightened with white, squared for transfer,
on pink tinted paper, some losses

12½ x 7¼ inches
318 x 185 mm

Provenance

Sir Peter Lely (L.2092)
Prosper Henry Lankrink (L. 2090)
Earl of Pembroke (sale: Sotheby's July 9, 1917, no. 397/5, as School of Raphael)

Literature

Strong, *op. cit.*, no. 59
Frommel, *op. cit.*

**AUTHORSHIP. Ascribed to the named artist—subject to the qualifications set forth in
the GLOSSARY and CONDITIONS OF SALE, front of this Catalogue.*

12

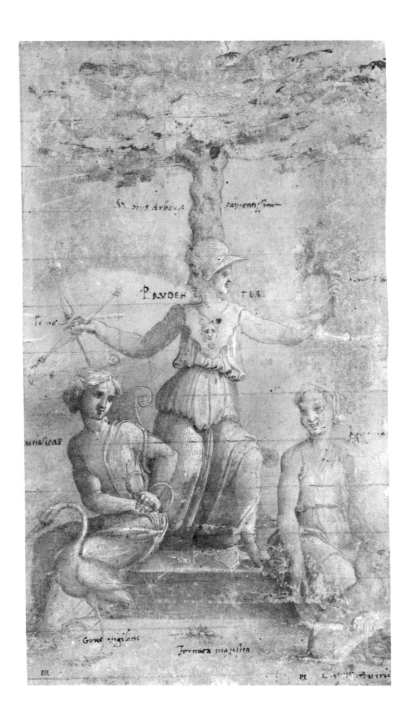

*BALDASSARE PERUZZI

8 *AN ALLEGORY OF FORTITUDE*
pen and brown ink and brown wash, heightened with white, squared for transfer, on pink tinted paper, some losses

12½ x 7¼ *inches*
318 x 185 *mm*

Provenance

Sir Peter Lely (L. 2092)
Prosper Henry Lankrink (L. 2090)
Earl of Pembroke (sale: Sotheby's July 9, 1917, no. 397/5, as School of Raphael)

Literature

Strong, *op. cit.,* no. 59
Frommel, *op. cit.*

*BALDASSARE PERUZZI

9 *AN ALLEGORY OF TEMPERANCE*
*pen and brown ink and brown wash, heightened with white, squared for transfer,
on pink tinted paper, some losses*

12½ x 7¼ inches
318 x 185 mm

Provenance

Sir Peter Lely (L. 2092)
Prosper Henry Lankrink (L. 2090)
Earl of Pembroke (sale: Sotheby's, July 9, 1917, no. 397/5, as School of Raphael)

Literature

Strong, *op. cit.,* no. 59
Frommel, *op. cit.*

*AUTHORSHIP. Ascribed to the named artist—subject to the qualifications set forth in
the GLOSSARY and CONDITIONS OF SALE, front of this Catalogue.*

*ORAZIO SAMMACCHINI

10 *THE FLAGELLATION*
pen and brown ink and brown wash, with an old attribution: S. del Piombo, some
losses and repairs

15¾ x 12½ *inches*
422 x 318 *mm*

Provenance

Jules Dupan (L. 1440)
Comte Gelozzi (L. 513)
Bonaffe and Alphonse Kann (sale: New York, American Art Association, January 7, 1927,
    no. 14, illus.)

*ESIAS VAN DE VELDE

11 *THE CRUCIFIXION*
black chalk and brown wash, signed and dated 1626, with framing lines

11½ x 12¾ *inches*
290 x 323 *mm*

*FRANCESCO GUARDI

12 *THE PIAZZA S. MARCO SEEN FROM THE PIAZZETTA DEI
LEONCINI*
pen and brown ink and grey wash, some losses repaired

10 x 10⅛ inches
255 x 258 mm

Another drawing by Francesco Guardi of the same view is in the Berlin Print Room
(Reproduced in J. Byam Shaw, *The Drawings of Francesco Guardi,* London, 1951,
no. 22)

*GIOVANNI BATTISTA TIEPOLO

13 *CHRIST CALLING THE FISHERMEN*
pen and brown ink and brown wash, over black chalk

16½ x 11½ *inches*
420 x 290 *mm*

Provenance

Prince Alexis Orloff (sale: Paris, Galerie Georges Petit, April 29/30, 1920, no. 93)
Albert Mayer

Literature

Seymour de Ricci, *Collection Albert Mayer,* Paris, 1935, no. 94

*AUTHORSHIP. Ascribed to the named artist—subject to the qualifications set forth in
the* GLOSSARY *and* CONDITIONS OF SALE, *front of this Catalogue.*

VENETIAN SCHOOL, 18TH CENTURY

14 *S. GIORGIO MAGGIORE*
*pen and brown ink and watercolor; pasted on the verso: a heart-shaped label
inscribed Prospetto di S. Giorgio Maggiore/Disegno framo. Guardi/Venezia*

10¼ x 16⅝ *inches*
260 x 423 *mm*

Provenance

Alfred Beardeley (L. 421)

*FRANCESCO BARTOLOZZI

15 *STUDY OF A YOUNG WOMAN*
red and black chalks, signed

8¾ x 7¼ *inches*
222 x 184 *mm*

(See illustration)

*FRANCESCO BARTOLOZZI

16 *TWO WOMEN WITH A CHILD*
red and black chalks, signed

9¼ x 6½ *inches*
235 x 165 *mm*

*FRANCESCO BARTOLOZZI

17 *MADONNA AND CHILD*
red and black chalks

9⅛ x 8 *inches*
231 x 203 *mm*

**AUTHORSHIP. Ascribed to the named artist—subject to the qualifications set forth in
the GLOSSARY and CONDITIONS OF SALE, front of this Catalogue.*

28

*CORNEILLE DE SPAENDONCK

18 *A VASE OF SUMMER FLOWERS AND FRUIT,* including roses, syringa and
grapes on a ledge, *gouache, signed, circular*

diameter: 3⅛ *inches*
80 *mm*

*MAURICE QUENTIN DE LA TOUR

19 *PORTRAIT OF MADAME DE LAFRETE,* the head, seen full face, *pastel, on buff paper, oval*

$8\frac{5}{8}$ x 6 *inches*
220 x 149 *mm*

A poem inscribed on the old mount:
'L 'Himen s'applaudissoit de vous trouver si belle,
il insultoit l'amour, le Dieu lui repartir,
frère crois moi, n'ayons pointe de querelle,
Si je t'abondonnois, ton pouvoir est detruit'.   Sireüil

*JEAN ANTOINE WATTEAU

20 *STUDIES OF A GIRL SEATED ON A BANK,* a young man lying behind her points over her shoulder, *red, black and white chalks, with an old attribution: Vataux fec, on buff paper*

9½ x 13¾ inches
240 x 350 mm

Provenance

Anonymous sale: Paris 1892, no. 72
Lallemand (sale: May 1894)
Léon Michel-Levy (sale: Paris, Galerie Georges Petit, June 17/18, 1925, no. 106)
George Blumenthal, New York

Exhibition

London, Royal Academy, 1932, *Exhibition of French Art,* no. 738, cat. no. 780 (lent by George Blumenthal)

Literature

Les Maîtres du Dessin, Paris, 1911, vol. III, pl. 136
K. T. Parker, *The Drawings of Antoine Watteau,* London, 1931, no. 92
K. T. Parker and J. Mathey, *Antoine Watteau, Catalogue complet de son oeuvre dessiné,* Paris, 1957, no. 665, reproduced

The study of the man was used in the painting *La Famille* (Dacier-Vauflart no. 86) and in *L'Assemblée galante* (D-V no. 139)
A document of 1777 makes it possible to identify the sitters in the painting, *La Famille,* as coming from the family of Sr. Leboucq-Santussan (see: Parker-Mathey, *op. cit.,* note to no. 665)

*JEAN ANTOINE WATTEAU

21 *A YOUNG GIRL LOOKING DOWN,* head and shoulders, *red and black chalks*

8¼ x 5¾ *inches*
208 x 146 *mm*

Provenance

Philippe Wiener
Albert Mayer (sale: 1935, no. 100)

Exhibition

London, Royal Academy, 1932, *Exhibition of French Art,* no. 713, cat. no. 765 (lent by
   Albert Mayer)

Literature

E. de Goncourt, *Catalogue raisonné de l'oeuvre peint, dessiné et gravé de Watteau,* 1875,
   no. 652 (the engraving)
Seymour de Ricci, *Collection Albert Mayer,* Paris, 1935, no. 100
K. T. Parker and J. Mathey, *Antoine Watteau, catalogue complet de son oeuvre dessiné,*
   Paris, 1957, no. 577, reproduced

   The head was engraved by Comte de Caylus, *Figures de différentes caractères,*
   no. 273

*JACQUES ANDRE PORTAIL

22 *A CONCERT PARTY OF LADIES AND GENTLEMEN*
    red and black chalks

10⅞ x 11⅛ *inches*
300 x 283 *mm*

Provenance

Labardier de Tinan
Pierre Decourcelle (sale: 1911, no. 139)
E. M. Hodgkins (sale: Paris, April 30, 1914)
Albert Mayer

Literature

Seymour de Ricci, *Collection Albert Mayer*, Paris, 1935, no. 71

*JACQUES ANDRE PORTAIL

23 *STUDIES OF A GIRL WEARING A FEATHERED HAT* and drawing on a sheet of paper, and a study of the arm of a lady, *red and black chalks, with framing lines, inscribed with attribution: Portail*

5⅛ x 6⅜ *inches*
130 x 163 mm

Provenance

General de Tavernot
J. Gigoux
Albert Mayer

Literature

Seymour de Ricci, *Collection Albert Mayer*, Paris, 1935, no. 72

AUTHORSHIP. Ascribed to the named artist—subject to the qualifications set forth in the GLOSSARY and CONDITIONS OF SALE, front of this Catalogue.

40

*LOUIS CARROGIS DE CARMONTELLE

24 *THE CRAYMOYEL FAMILY,* a young man balances his child, standing on a chair and holding its mother's hand, in an ornamental garden, *watercolor, over red chalk*

13 x 9 inches
330 x 230 mm

Provenance

Albert Mayer

Exhibitions

Paris, Galerie André Weil, *Carmontelle,* 1933, no. 10
Rotterdam, Museum Boymans van Beuningen, *Van Clouet tot Matisse,* 1958, no. 39, reproduced in the catalogue, pl. 78

Literature

Seymour de Ricci, *Collection Albert Mayer,* Paris, 1935, no. 17, reproduced

Inscribed in ink: Mr et Mde de Cramoyel avec leur charmant petit garçon. Tableau de famille plein d'expression et de vérité, dessiné par M. Carmontel.

AUTHORSHIP. Ascribed to the named artist—subject to the qualifications set forth in the GLOSSARY *and* CONDITIONS OF SALE, *front of this Catalogue.*

42

*LOUIS CARROGIS DE CARMONTELLE

25 *A PORTRAIT OF THE DUC DE COGNI*, three-quarter length, in profile, fac-
ing to the right, *red and black chalks, inscribed on the verso in ink: Mr. le duc de
Cogni mestre de Campe qual des dragons desiné par Carmontel aide de Camps du
Regimt colonel d'Orleans Iveryom en 1757*

6⅝ x 4⅝ *inches*
170 x 118 *mm*

Provenance

Jean Masson (L. 1494 a)

*AUTHORSHIP. Ascribed to the named artist—subject to the qualifications set forth in
the GLOSSARY and CONDITIONS OF SALE, front of this Catalogue.*

44

*FRANÇOIS BOUCHER

26 *PORTRAIT OF A YOUNG LADY,* head and shoulders, inclined to the right
and looking down, *pastel*

9⅞ x 7¼ *inches*
250 x 185 *mm*

Provenance

Albert Mayer

Exhibitions

Paris, Galerie Charpentier, June 1932, *Exposition Boucher,* no. 120
London, Royal Academy, 1932, *Exhibition of French Art,* no. 762, cat. no. 649 (lent by
Albert Mayer)

Literature

Seymour de Ricci, *Collection Albert Mayer,* Paris, 1935, no. 12

Engraved by De Marteau

A similar drawing was formerly in the J. P. Heseltine Collection (reproduced in
A. Ananoff, *L'oeuvre dessiné de Boucher,* Paris, 1966, fig. 64)

*FRANÇOIS BOUCHER

27 *HEAD OF A YOUNG GIRL,* full face, turned to the left, her eyes looking towards the right, *red, black and white chalks*

6⅞ x 5½ *inches*
175 x 140 *mm*

Provenance

Philippe Wiener
Albert Mayer

Exhibitions

Paris, Galerie Charpentier, June 1932, *Exposition Boucher,* no. 119

Literature:

Seymour de Ricci, *Collection Albert Mayer,* Paris, 1935, no. 13

*JEAN BAPTISTE HUET

28 *PORTRAIT OF A GIRL,* wearing a large hat, full face, turned slightly towards
the left, *gouache, oval*

$9\frac{7}{8} \times 4\frac{7}{8}$ *inches*
250 x 125 mm

Provenance

Philippe Wiener
Albert Mayer

*CLAUDE HOIN

29 *THE HEADS OF TWO MEN,* that on the left possibly Jean-Honoré Fragonard,
black and white chalks, on blue paper

$14\frac{7}{8}$ x 20 *inches*
379 x 509 *mm*

Provenance

Paul Royer-Bollard
George Blumenthal, New York

Exhibitions

Paris, Galerie André Weil, *Claude Hoin, Peintre de Monsieur,* 1934, no. 47
Rotterdam, Museum Boymans van Beuningen, *Van Clouet tot Matisse,* 1958, no. 61, reproduced in the catalogue, pl. 85

Literature

R. Portalis, *Gazette des Beaux-Arts,* vol. XXIII, 1900, p. 207, illus.
R. Portalis, *Claude Hoin,* 1900, p. 42
S. R. Bloch, *Catalogue of the Collection of George and Florence Blumenthal,* Paris, 1930,
vol. V, pl. XXXV

**AUTHORSHIP. Ascribed to the named artist—subject to the qualifications set forth in
the GLOSSARY and CONDITIONS OF SALE, front of this Catalogue.*

*JEAN HONORE FRAGONARD

30 *VISITE A LA NOURRICE,* an interior with a mother presenting her young
children to her bedridden nurse, *gray wash over black chalk*

12 x 15 inches
304 x 380 mm

Provenance

F. Villot (sale: 1859, no. 122)
Prince A. d'Arenberg
H. Walferdin (sale: April 12, 1880, no. 200)
E. H. Molyneux, Neuilly

Exhibitions

Berlin, Royal Academy, 1910, *Exposition d'Art Français du XVIIIe Siècle*
Paris, Musée Carnavalet, 1928, *La Vie Parisienne au XVIIIe Siècle,* no. 166
Paris, Galerie Jacques Seligmann, May 1931, *Exposition de Dessins de Fragonard,* no. 22

Literature

L. Reau, *Fragonard,* Brussels, 1956, p. 206

Another version of the same subject was formerly in the Collection of Arthur Veil-
Picard (reproduced in François Fosca, *Les Dessins de Fragonard,* Lausanne, 1954,
no. 6)
The subject is taken from the novel *Sarah Th.,* which was translated from the
English in 1765 by Saint-Lambert, the poet of the *Seasons* and friend of Grimm
and Mlle d'Houdetot.

*JEAN HONORE FRAGONARD

31 *'LE PETIT PREDICATEUR'*, a nursery scene with a child standing on a chest, supported by his mother and watched by an older woman surrounded by children, *brown wash, over black chalk*

13¾ x 18⅜ *inches*
349 x 467 *mm*

Provenance

Anonymous sale: May 31, 1790, no. 180
M. Marmontel (sale: Paris, January 25/26, 1883, no. 100, purchased by Clément for 1500 fr.)
Richard Lion (sale: April 3, 1886, no. 40)
M. P. Ledoux (sale: Paris, Galerie Georges Petit, March 5, 1918, no. 27, reproduced)
Adrien Fauchier-Magnan, Paris
Arthur Veil-Picard
Guiraud Brothers, Paris

Literature

R. Portalis, *Fragonard,* Paris 1889, pp. 200, 310
E. and J. de Goncourt, *L'Art du XVIIIe Siècle—Fragonard,* Paris, 1914, pp. 300-301
Connaissance des Arts, August 1956, reproduced, p. 42
L. Réau, *Fragonard,* Brussels, 1956, cat. p. 205, fig. 79
A. Ananoff, *L'Oeuvre dessiné de Fragonard,* Paris, 1961, vol. 1, no. 40, fig. 18

Engraved with variations by N. de Launay in 1781 as a pendant to *L'education fait tout,* now in the Collection of Baron E. de Rothschild (Ananoff, no. 11, fig. 6). This engraving may have been made from the painting of the same subject formerly in the Veil-Picard Collection (Wildenstein, no. 471)

*AUTHORSHIP. Ascribed to the named artist—subject to the qualifications set forth in the GLOSSARY *and* CONDITIONS OF SALE, *front of this Catalogue.*

56

*JEAN HONORE FRAGONARD

32 *LA LECTURE,* reputedly Madame Fragonard reading a letter to her sister, Marguerite Gérard, *brown wash, the corners rounded out*

11 x 8¼ *inches*
280 x 210 *mm*

Provenance

H. Walferdin (sale: Paris, April 12/16, 1880, no. 192, purchased by J. P. Heseltine for 550 fr.)
J. P. Heseltine, London
E. H. Molyneux, Neuilly

Exhibitions

London, *National Loan Exhibition,* 1909-1910, no. 99
Paris, Musée Carnavalet, *La Vie Parisienne au XVIIIe Siècle,* 1928, no. 165
Paris, Hotel de Sagan, *Fragonard,* 1931, no. 55 (lent by E. H. Molyneux)

Literature

R. Portalis, *Fragonard,* Paris, 1889, p. 307
[J. P. Heseltine] *Drawings by François Boucher, Jean-Honoré Fragonard in the Collection of J. P. Heseltine,* London, 1900, no. 4, (the engraving by J. de Goncourt was reproduced in place of the drawing)
J. P. Heseltine, *Dessins de l'Ecole française du XVIIIe siècle provenant de la Collection Heseltine,* Paris, 1913, no. 32, reproduced
A. Ananoff, *L'Oeuvre dessiné de Fragonard,* Paris, 1961, vol. 1, no. 62, fig. 28

An almost identical drawing of the same subject is in the Louvre (Ananoff, no. 61, fig. 27)

*JEAN HONORE FRAGONARD

33 *A YOUNG COUPLE SEATED AT A WRITING TABLE,* visited by a young
lady accompanied by her children and a nurse, *brown wash, over black chalk*

7⅛x 9⅛ *inches*
180 x 230 *mm*

Provenance

R. Owen, Paris

Exhibitions

Buffalo, Albright Art Gallery, *Master Drawings selected from the Museums and Private
Collections of America,* January 1934, (lent by Mrs J. I. Straus)

*JEAN HONORE FRAGONARD

34 '*LA REPRIMANDE DU GRAND-PAPA*', a child supported by his mother listens to the scolding of his grandfather, who is seated at a desk, *gray-brown wash, over black chalk*

13½ x 17¾ *inches*
345 x 450 *mm*

Provenance

Louis-Antoine-August Rohan-Chabot (sale: Paris, December 8, 1807, no. 43)
Baron Vivant-Denon (sale: Paris, May 1/19, 1826, no. 732, 9 fr.)

**AUTHORSHIP. Ascribed to the named artist—subject to the qualifications set forth in the* GLOSSARY *and* CONDITIONS OF SALE, *front of this Catalogue.*

62

*JEAN HONORE FRAGONARD

35 *LA VILLA ALDOBRANDINI,* with figures playing beside the fountain, *red chalk*

14 x 18½ inches
355 x 468 mm

Provenance

R. Owen, Paris

Exhibitions

Paris, Petit Palais, *Le Paysage français de Poussin à Corot,* May-June 1925, no. D. 442

A contre épreuve of this drawing, attributed to Hubert Robert, is at Orléans.

*HUBERT ROBERT

36 *THE ENTRANCE TO THE VILLA ALDOBRANDINI*
watercolor and brown wash, over black chalk

18⅞ x 19½ *inches*
480 x 495 *mm*

*HUBERT ROBERT

37 *PEASANT GIRLS IN A BOAT CROSSING A RIVER*, a castle on a hill in the
background, *pen and black ink and gray wash over red chalk*

8½ x 12½ *inches*
216 x 318 *mm*

Provenance

H. W. Campe
Professor Ernst Ehlers (sale: Leipzig, Boerner, May 9/10, 1930, no. 352)

*JEAN BAPTISTE MARECHAL

38 *A VIEW OF THE GARDENS OF THE TUILERIES,* with an elegant company promenading, *pen and brown ink and watercolor, signed and dated 1788*

8 x 12½ inches
202 x 318 mm

Provenance

Noel Bardac, Paris
Destailleur (sale: Paris, Hôtel des Commissaires—Priseurs, May 21, 1896, no. 644, illus.)
E. H. Molyneux, Neuilly

Literature

L'Illustration, June 20, 1928, "Les Peintres des jardins à la Bagatelle" (as "Le Jardin des Tuileries au XVIIIe Siècle")

*LOUIS GABRIEL MOREAU L'AINE

39 *LES BAIGNEUSES,* with two young girls bathing in a pond by a ruined colon-
nade; and *LE TEMPLE CIRCULAIRE,* with elegant company resting by a
rotunda, *gouache, a pair*

each: 15⅝ x 12¼ *inches*
397 x 310 *mm*

Provenance

Albert Mayer

Exhibitions

London, Royal Academy, *Exhibition of French Art,* 1932, no. 806, cat. no. 717 *(Les
Baigneuses* only)

Literature

Seymour de Ricci, *Collection Albert Mayer,* Paris, 1935, nos. 55, 56

*LOUIS GABRIEL MOREAU L'AINE

40 *ELEGANT COMPANY IN A PARK NEAR A LAKE* and *ELEGANT COM-
PANY BOATING ON A LAKE*
gouache on vellum, a pair, ovals

9⅝ x 7½ *inches*
245 x 190 *mm*

Provenance

La Duchesse de Trevise (sale: Paris, May 7, 1917, no. 24)

Literature

G. Wildenstein, *Louis Moreau L'Ainé,* Paris, 1923, p. 67, no. 142

> Inscribed on the verso of both frames: Gouache de Louis Moreau acheté chez
> Gasquet. One continues: Rue *** (Aubert?) pres de rue du Port Mahon Bve
> Hausmann. There is another inscription above the first drawing: de chez Lebland
> percepteur du duc

**AUTHORSHIP. Ascribed to the named artist—subject to the qualifications set forth in
the* GLOSSARY *and* CONDITIONS OF SALE, *front of this Catalogue.*

74

*LOUIS GABRIEL MOREAU L'AINE

41   *A LANDSCAPE WITH A POND,* with two figures in the foreground; beyond, a
     cottage surrounded by trees with other figures, *gouache, on the verso of the frame*
     an old label with L. Moreau no. 1, 196

12⅜ x 19 inches
315 x 483 mm

Provenance

R. Owen, Paris

*LOUIS GABRIEL MOREAU L'AINE

42 *ELEGANT COMPANY BY A FOUNTAIN IN A PARK*
gouache, signed with monogram

9⅞ x 14⅜ inches
250 x 365 mm

Provenance

Duke of Littia, Milan

*LOUIS GABRIEL MOREAU L'AINE

43 *A CHATEAU NEAR A STREAM IN A WOODED PLAIN* and *A COTTAGE BY A STREAM WITH A GATE INTO A WOOD*
gouache, signed with monogram, a pair

5¼ x 8½ *inches*
134 x 214 *mm*

*LOUIS-GABRIEL MOREAU L'AINE

44   *THE TERRACE OF A PARK,* with steps flanked by vases leading up to the terrace, *gouache on vellum*

7⅞ x 11 inches
200 x 280 mm

Provenance

Jean-François Gigoux (L. 1164) (sale: Paris, March 20, 1882, no. 678)
Albert Mayer

Exhibitions

London, Royal Academy, *Exhibition of French Art,* 1932, no. 810, cat. no. 718 (lent by
   Albert Mayer)

Literature

Seymour de Ricci, *Collection Albert Mayer,* Paris, 1935, no. 60

45 *LES TROIS SOEURS AU PARC DE SAINT CLOUD*
    watercolor and gray wash, signed

$6\frac{5}{8} \times 8\frac{5}{8}$ *inches*
168 x 218 mm

Provenance

Audouin, Paris (January 18, 1892)
M. G. Muhlbacher (sale: Paris, Galerie Georges Petit, May 15/18, 1899, no. 166, 3,550 fr. The preceding lot no. 165 formed the pair, entitled: "les graces Parisiennes au Bois de Vincennes", and sold for 4,750 fr.)
E. M. Hodgkins (sale: Paris, April 30, 1914, no. 38)

Engraved by J. P. Chapuy and Vidal with the title: "Le Bosquet d'Amour"

AUTHORSHIP. Ascribed to the named artist—subject to the qualifications set forth in the GLOSSARY and CONDITIONS OF SALE, front of this Catalogue.

84

*NICOLAS LAVREINCE

46 *L'AMOUR FRIVOLE,* a young man leans through a window to lift the fichu of a girl who sits asleep at her dressing table, *gouache*

11⅜ x 8½ *inches*
290 x 215 *mm*

Provenance

Pierre Decourcelle
Albert Mayer

> This drawing was engraved by Beuvarlet, with the title: "L'Amour Frivole". Inscribed on the verso of the frame:
> Cette gouache, dont tous les inconographes ont placé la gravure fait d'après cet original dans l'oeuvre de Baudouin a été montrée à Monsieur Edmond de Goncourt par Monsieur Pierre Decourcelle le 18 Mars 1895.
> Monsieur Edmond de Goncourt qui possède l'une des plus belles collections de dessins originaux des Maîtres du XVIIIième a affirmé à Monsieur Pierre Decourcelle que cette pièce était faussement attribuée à Baudouin et qu'elle était l'oeuvre de Lavreince.   Greppe.

*JEAN BAPTISTE MALLET

47   *TWO INTERIORS,* with two young girls, one standing and holding a muff; and
     two young girls, one seated, the other wearing a shawl, *gouache, a pair*

     11⅝ x 8¾ *inches*
     295 x 224 *mm*

*JEAN BAPTISTE ISABEY

48 *PORTRAIT OF THE COMPOSER ANDRE GRETRY,*
   black and white chalks, gray wash, signed and inscribed with the identity of the
   sitter, within an oval

15 *x* 11⅝ *inches*
380 *x* 268 *mm*

André Ernest Modeste Grétry (1741-1813), author and musician, best known for
his operas, *Guillaume Tell* and *Richard Coeur de Lion.*

*JEAN AUGUSTE DOMINIQUE INGRES

49 *PORTRAIT OF MRS CHARLES BADHAM, NEE MARGARET CAMPBELL,*
seated, holding a book, the Villa Medici in the background, *graphite, signed and dated Rome 1816*

10¼ x 8¼ *inches*
261 x 210 *mm*

Provenance

Charles Badham (d. 1845)
The Badham Family
C. Badham-Jackson (sale: Sotheby's, December 12, 1928, no. 145, reproduced, purchased
by Dr. Borenius)
Wildenstein and Co., Inc., New York, 1929

Exhibitions

New York, Paul Rosenberg Gallery, *Ingres in American Collections,* 1961, reproduced in
the catalogue, no. 22
Cambridge, Massachusetts, Fogg Art Museum, *Ingres Centennial Exhibition,* 1967, reproduced in the catalogue, no. 37

Literature

Morton D. Zabel, 'Ingres in America', in *The Arts,* February 1930, vol. XVI, p. 378,
reproduced
Jean Cassou, 'Ingres et ses Contradictions' in *Gazette des Beaux-Arts,* March 1934, vol. XI,
p. 157, fig. 15
Brinsley Ford, 'Ingres Portrait Drawings of English People at Rome', in *The Burlington
Magazine,* July 1939, vol. LXXV, pp. 8 ff., pl. 111 C
Hans Naef, *Rome vue par Ingres,* Lausanne, 1960, p. 27, fig. 52

In 1815 the Badhams, who lived in the Via Gregoriana 25, were close neighbours
of Ingres, who lived at no. 34 of the same street. Charles Badham, a distinguished
physician, was also a gifted Latinist and passionate traveler. Between 1815-17, he
traveled in the lesser known regions of Southern Italy and throughout Greece,
leaving his wife and children in Rome.

His wife, born Margaret Campbell, was a noted beauty, a first cousin of the poet
Thomas Campbell who seems to have sued for her hand unsuccessfully. She was
thirty-five years of age when Ingres drew her, seated at the head of the Via Gregoriana with the Villa Medici and the obelisk at the top of the Spanish steps in
the background.   (biographical information from the Fogg catalogue, *op. cit.*)

*AUTHORSHIP. Ascribed to the named artist—subject to the qualifications set forth in
the* GLOSSARY *and* CONDITIONS OF SALE, *front of this Catalogue.*

Ingres. Del Roma 1816.

*HILAIRE GERMAIN EDGAR DEGAS

50 *PORTRAIT OF MONSIEUR JACQUET*, seen at full face, *pastel, signed*

10¼ x 8¼ *inches*
260 x 209 *mm*

Provenance

Professor Herman Heilbuth, Copenhagen

Literature

Jean Sutherland Boggs, *Portraits by Degas,* University of California Press, 1962, p. 120
   (wherein the drawing is dated *circa* 1878)

*AUTHORSHIP. *Ascribed to the named artist—subject to the qualifications set forth in
   the* GLOSSARY *and* CONDITIONS OF SALE, *front of this Catalogue.*

[END OF SALE]

PARKE-BERNET & SOTHEBY OFFICES

NEW YORK
Parke-Bernet Galleries · Inc
980 Madison Ave., N.Y. 10021
Telephone 212/879-8300
Telex New York 222643
Telegram Parkgal, New York

Sotheby's of London Ltd.
980 Madison Ave., N.Y. 10021
Telephone 212/758-2891
Telex New York 222643
Telegram Abinitio, New York

LONDON
Sotheby & Co
34/35 New Bond Street
London, W1A 2AA
Telephone 01-493-8080
Telex London 24454
Telegram Abinitio, London

CALIFORNIA
Representative for
Sotheby's of London Ltd.
Miss Philippa Calnan
The Executive Life Building
Suite 904
9777 Wilshire Boulevard
Beverly Hills, Cal. 90210
Telephone 213/274-7329
Telex 677120

TEXAS
Representative for
**Parke-Bernet Galleries · Inc
and Sotheby & Co**
Edward J. Landrigan, III
Post Oak Tower
5051 Westheimer Road
Houston, Texas 77027
Telephone 713/623-0010
Telex PB HOU 762275

ARGENTINA
Representative for
Sotheby & Co *and*
Parke-Bernet Galleries · Inc
William R. Edbrooke
Kerteux Antiquités
Libertad 846
Buenos Aires, Argentina
Telephone 41 Plaza 0831

AUSTRALIA
**Sotheby & Co (Australia)
Pty. Ltd.**
Representing
Sotheby & Co *and*
Parke-Bernet Galleries · Inc
13th Floor, Prince Gate
171 Flinders Street
Melbourne, Victoria 3000
Telephone 63-6643
Telegram Abinitio, Melbourne

CANADA
Sotheby & Co (Canada) Ltd.
Geoffrey P. Joyner
Representing
Sotheby & Co *and*
Parke-Bernet Galleries · Inc
P.O. Box 305
Suite 2230, Royal Trust Tower
Toronto Dominion Centre
Toronto 111, Ontario
Telephone 416/363-6353
Telegram Abinitio, Toronto

FRANCE
Representative for
Southby & Co *and*
Parke-Bernet Galleries · Inc
Valentin Abdy
8 Rue de Duras, Paris 8e
Telephone ANJOU 2599

ITALY
Representative for
Sotheby & Co *and*
Parke-Bernet Galleries · Inc
Dr. A. Chesne Dauphiné
Via Leone X, 4
50129 Florence
Telephone 47-49-25
Telegram Abinitio, Florence

LEBANON
Representative for
Sotheby & Co *and*
Parke-Bernet Galleries · Inc
Mounir Atallah
Eldorado Buildings, Apt. 310
Post Office Box 7095
Hamra Street, Beirut
Telephone 257970/257105
Telegram Auctionart, Beirut

SOUTH AFRICA
Representative for
Sotheby & Co *and*
Parke-Bernet Galleries · Inc
Reinhold H. Cassirer
11/17 Jorissen Street
Braamfontein, Johannesburg
P.O. Box 31010
Telephone 724-5967
Telegram Abinitio,
Johannesburg

SWITZERLAND
Representative for
Sotheby & Co *and*
Parke-Bernet Galleries · Inc
Dr. J. G. Wille
in partnership with
Alfred Schwarzenbach
18 Bleicherweg, 8022. Zurich
Telephone (010 41 51) 250011
Cable Abinitio, Zurich
Telex 52380

WEST GERMANY
Representative for
Sotheby & Co *and*
Parke-Bernet Galleries · Inc
Valentin Abdy
8000 Munich 22
Galeriestrasse 6A
Telephone 29-2252

PB

PARKE-BERNET GALLERIES • INC

designs its catalogues and directs
all details of illustration, text
and typography

PHOTOGRAPHS BY TAYLOR & DULL • NEW YORK

PRINTED IN THE U.S.A. BY
DAVIS-DELANEY-ARROW INC.
NEW YORK